It doesn't matter if the car is automatic or stick,
His name may be Richard, but he drives like a Dic

Weaving in and out of lanes makes his passengers sick
His name may be Richard, but he drives like a Dick.

Doing 60 in a 30 is a little too quick,
His name may be Richard, but he drives like a Dic

He doesn't wear a seatbelt – never a click,
His name may be Richard, but he drives like a Dick

He's eating ice cream and taking a lick,
His name may be Richard, but he drives like a Dic

He never uses the signals – not even one tick,
His name may be Richard, but he drives like a Dick

His music is blaring – you can feel the bass kick,
His name may be Richard, but he drives like a Dic

He's texting while driving and thinking he's slick,
His name may be Richard, but he drives like a Dick

He's screaming and cursing and waving his fist,
His name may be Richard, but he drives like a Dic

He's tailgating you and has a bone to pick,
His name may be Richard, but he drives like a Dick

He cut you off in traffic – you almost crash in a ditch
His name may be Richard, but he drives like a Dick.

There were no more spots so he made his car fit,
His name may be Richard, but he drives like a Dick

So take my advice, it will do the trick –
If you are going somewhere in the car on a trip,
Don't let Richard drive, because Richard's a Dick!

CPSIA information can be obtained
at www.ICGtesting.com
Printed in the USA
LVHW072138140821
695342LV00002B/22